# Chicken
# Dip

## and other stories

Marie Birkinshaw

Lorraine Horsley

Shirley Jackson

Mandy Ross

Written by:
Marie Birkinshaw    (pp.6–7, 16–17, 42–43, 44–45)

Lorraine Horsley    (pp.12–13, 14–15, 18–19, 20–21, 22–23)

Shirley Jackson    (pp.8–11)

Mandy Ross    (pp.4–5, 24–28, 29–36, 37–39, 40–41, 46–48)

Illustrated by:
Adrian Barclay    (pp.16–17, 29–36, 44–45)

Phillip Burrows    (pp.4–5, 14–15, 37–39)

Andrew Everitt-Stewart    (pp.6–7, 20–21, 40–41)

Mary Hall    (pp.12–13, 22–23, 46–48)

David Mostyn    (pp.8–11, 18–19, 24–28, 42–43)

Cover illustration by Adrian Barclay

Designed by Anne Matthews

Project Co-ordinator: Fran Stevens

Text ©    Marie Birkinshaw, Lorraine Horsley, Shirley Jackson, Mandy Ross, 2005

© BASS 2005

Published by   BASS publications 2005
Martineau Centre, Balden Road,
Harborne, Birmingham B32 2EH
ISBN: 1-898244-95-2

# Contents

The trip     4

A new pet     6

Night time/Day time     8

Time for bed     12

Are we there yet?     14

Chicken dip     16

I am     18

My brother     20

My sister     22

All get in     24

What is this?     29

Balls?     37

Sports     40

Detectives!     42

Juggling     44

I like...     46

# The trip

6

# Night time/Day time

day time

play time

home time

tea time

bed time

night time

night time

play time

tea time

10

home time

bed time

day time

11

# Time for bed

13

# Are we there yet?

# I am

I am a boy.

I am a girl.

I am
a brother.

I am
a sister.

I am a man.     I am a woman.

I am a dad.     I am a mum.

We are a family.

19

# My brother

My brother gave me his football.

My brother gave me his bike.

My brother gave me his chips.

My brother gave me his chicken pox!

# My sister

I love football.

Just like my sister!

I love chips.

Just like my sister!

I love cats.

Just like my sister!

I am cool.

Just like my sister!

# All get in

25

# What is this?

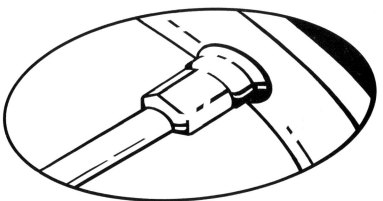

What is this? Can you see?

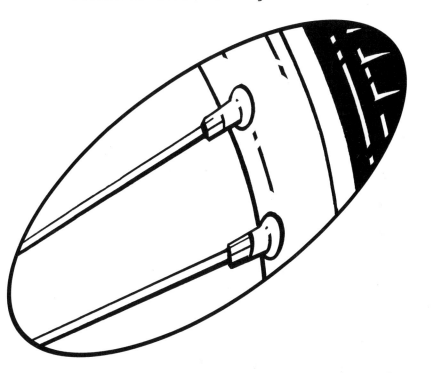

Here is some more. What can it be?

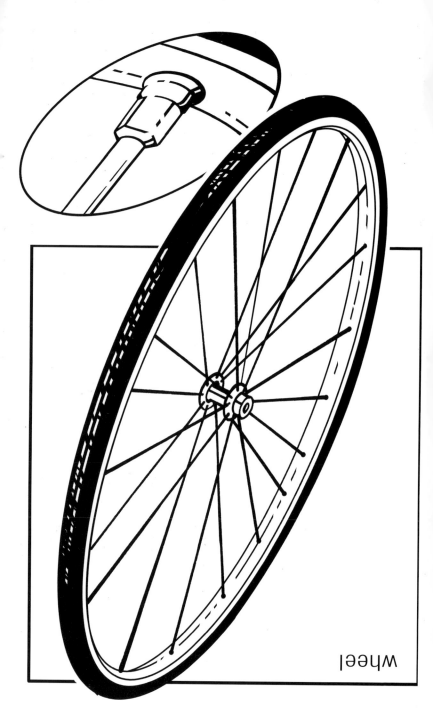

wheel

And what is this? Can you see?

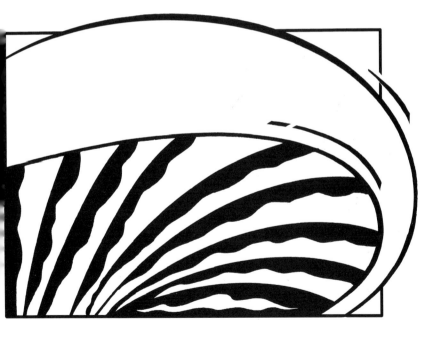

Here is some more. What can it be?

mushroom

# What is this? Can you see?

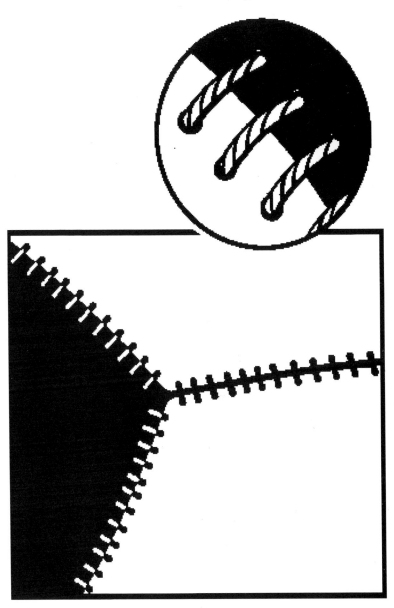

Here is some more. What can it be?

football

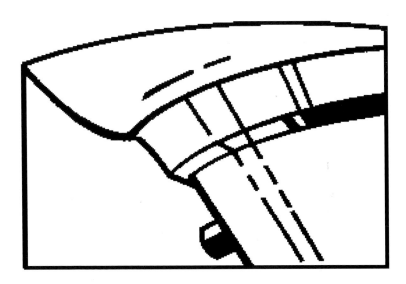

And what is this? Can you see?

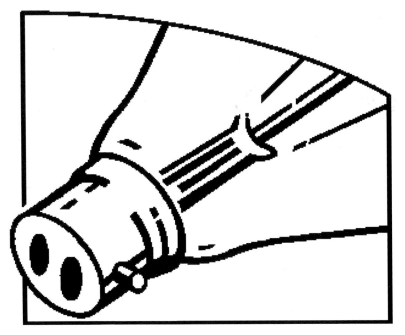

Here is some more. What can it be?

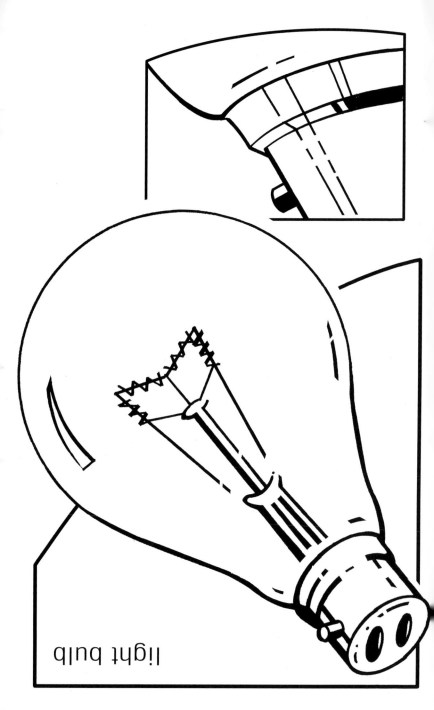

light bulb

# *Balls?*

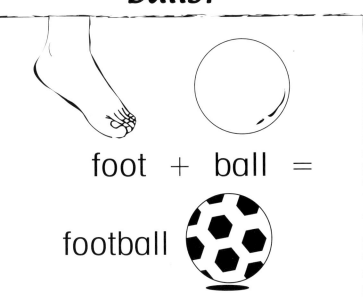

foot + ball =

football

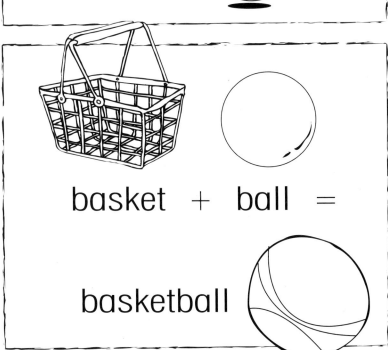

basket + ball =

basketball

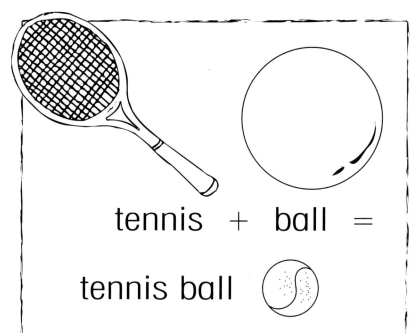

tennis + ball =

tennis ball

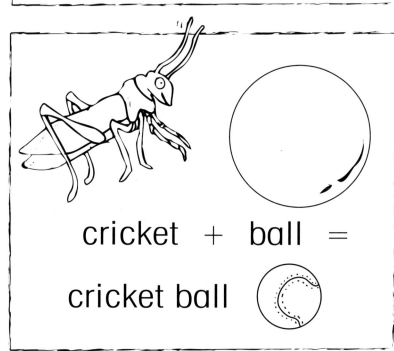

cricket + ball =

cricket ball

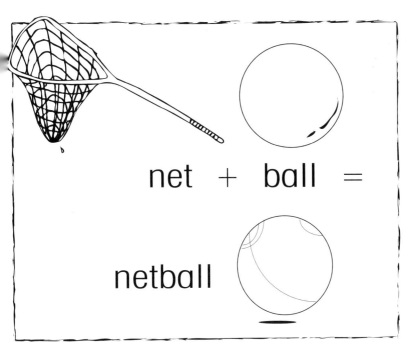

net + ball =

netball

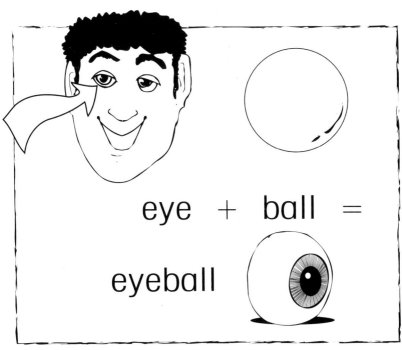

eye + ball =

eyeball

# Sports

## Can you play football?

## Can you play cricket?

Can you play netball?

Can you play tennis?

Can you play basketball?

# Detectives

The first night we saw footprints.

The next night we saw fingerprints.

The next night we saw crumbs.

The next night we saw you!

# Juggling

I like pizza for my tea.

My dad likes football and...

...my mum likes me.